D1401353

Growing in Faith

Seven Stories for Children

Growing In Faith

Seven Stories
for Children

Written
and illustrated by
Helen Caswell

Abingdon Press

Nashville

Growing in Faith
Seven Stories for Children

Compilation Copyright © 1998 by Abingdon Press
All Rights Reserved

Text and Illustrations from *God Makes Us Different*
Copyright © 1988 by Helen Caswell

Text and Illustrations from *God Must Like to Laugh*
Copyright © 1987 by Abingdon Press

Text and Illustrations from *I Can Talk with God*
Copyright © 1989 by Abingdon Press

Text and Illustrations from *I Know Who Jesus Is*
Copyright © 1989 by Abingdon Press

Text and Illustrations from *My Big Family at Church*
Copyright © 1989 by Abingdon Press

Text and Illustrations from *God Is Always with Me*
Copyright © 1989 by Abingdon Press

Text and Illustratins from *God's Love Is for Sharing*
Copyright © 1987 by Abingdon Press

ISBN 0-7394-0199-8

Printed in Hong Kong

Contents

God Makes
Us Different

There isn't anybody just like me,
because God makes everybody different.

7

I guess when God has to make so many people,
it's more fun to make them different.

It would be boring to make them all the same.
So he makes us different colours—
brown and pink and tan.

And he makes all shapes and sizes.

And he puts curly hair on some and straight hair on others.

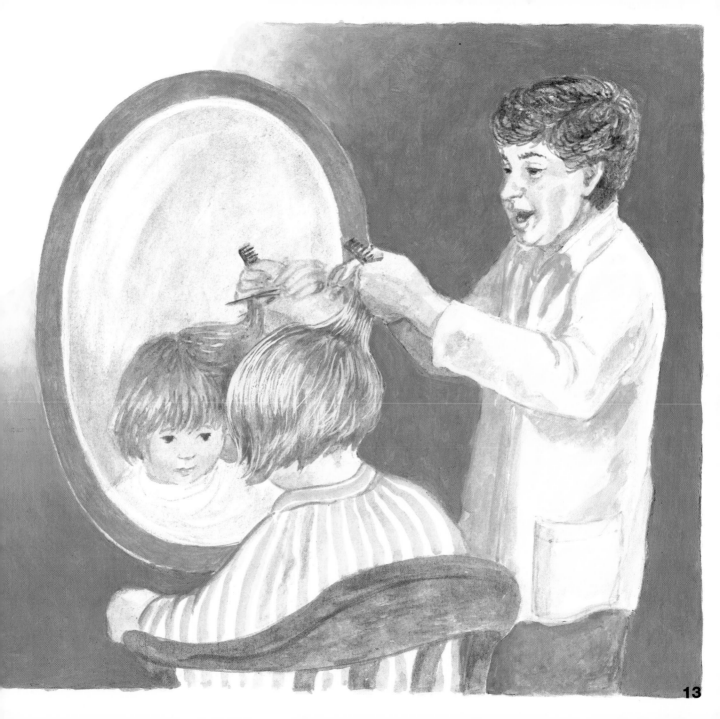

And some are boys and some are girls.

God makes some noisy ones and some quiet ones.

But though people look different on the outside, on the inside, we are not different at all.

Everybody likes to eat.

And everybody needs to sleep.

Everybody cries, sometimes.

And everybody likes to laugh.

So I guess God makes our outsides all different, just for fun.
But he makes our insides all alike,
  and he loves us, every one.

God Must
Like to Laugh

God made the world—the heavens, too—
And night and day, and me and you.

But along with big things like the sun,
God must have had a lot of fun

Attending to each small detail:
The fragile shell upon the snail,

The flowers fitted to the bee,
And little bugs too small to see,

The camels and the kangaroos,
And things you only see in zoos,

The penguin and the platypus,
The monstrous hippopotamus,

The wondrous webs the spiders spin,

The way cats purr, the way dogs grin.

And just because God took a notion,
We have whales spouting in the ocean.

We have the llama and the shrew,
The green bullfrog and peacocks blue,

And snakes and bats and all those others
That only God could love—or mothers.

How would God think up all those things?
The different song that each bird sings,

The cockatoo and crocodile—
I think they must have made God smile.
It must have been the way he played.

And when at last they all were made,
From tiny gnat to tall giraffe,
I wish I could have heard God laugh!

—

I Can Talk to God

I can talk with God.

In the morning when I get up,
I thank God for the new day,
even if it's raining.

I thank God for my orange juice and cereal and my toast with jelly on it.

Some days I feel so happy I just have to jump up and
down and thank God for the whole world
and especially me
and everything.

I ask God to take care of all of us.
I ask God for lots of things.
Sometimes the answer is yes, and sometimes the answer is no,
and sometimes God doesn't seem to answer me at all.

But maybe that's because I don't
listen well enough.
You have to listen very carefully,
because God doesn't talk to you like
your parents,
or your sister, or anybody.

God answers you inside your head. When I say, "Make my little sister good," I hear a little voice inside my head that makes me think, "My little sister copies me, so I have to be good *first*."

When I asked God for a pony,
the little voice said, "Where would you put it?"

If I feel sad or if I feel angry,
I talk to God about it, and then I feel better.

Sometimes it helps to get down on my knees and hold my hands together and close my eyes. Sometimes it's nice to pray with other people— lots of people all talking to God at once.

But best of all is when I'm in bed at night, in the dark,
and nobody's there but God and me,
and I can talk with God.

I Know
Who Jesus Is

To Jessica Caswell

Lots of times
I wonder about Jesus,
and how he lived on earth
a long time ago.
I wish I could have been there.

Jesus came as a little baby
so that he could be born like one
of us and live with us
here a while.

Jesus grew up
just like other boys.
Only, of course,
he was a lot more special.

Jesus liked sheep,
and he liked the shepherds
who took care of the little lambs.

He liked boats, too, and fishermen.

Sometimes they had fish-fries on the beach.

One time Jesus made a storm stop
because the fishermen were afraid.
He told them they must not be afraid,
because he was with them.

Even though Jesus had all the power of God,
he didn't go around moving mountains or anything like that.
He used his power for helping people.
He cured people who were sick
and made blind people see again.
Once a little girl was so sick she died,
but Jesus brought her back to life.

One day when a lot of people
had come to hear him talk, and
it was dinner time and there wasn't anything to eat,
Jesus took a few loaves of bread
and some little fish that a boy had brought
and turned them into enough food
to feed all those people.

I wish I had been that boy.

Jesus liked little children a lot.

And the children liked him, too.

He would hold them on his lap
and tell them stories.
I wish I could sit on Jesus' lap.

Even though Jesus went to heaven,
he's not very far away.
I can talk to him,
and sometimes I can almost feel
his hand in mine.

I know Jesus loves me.

My Big Family at Church

I like to go to church on Sunday morning.

All the church buildings are different.
Some have steeples pointing up to God,
and some have colored windows,
and some have bells ringing.

But each church is like a place
where a big family gets together.

My church family gets together every Sunday, and other days, too, to show God that we love him.

All sorts of people are in my church family.
Some make music for God.
I like to hear them singing.
I sing along:
Halleluja!
Amen!

Some teach Sunday school.
I like my teacher.
She tells us about camels
and good Samaritans
and Jesus.

Some people cook in the kitchen
when we have suppers for
our church family.
I like the chocolate cake.

Some of the people keep the church clean and beautiful.
I like to pick up the papers near the sidewalk.

Some go out to visit people who are sick or need help, and we collect things—like my extra clothes and toys to send to people who need them.

The people in my church family
are all different,
but we all work together
and love each other,
because we love God.

And God promised a long time ago
that when people get together
to show their love for him,
he will come and be there with them.

God Is Always with Me

I don't see why the good things can't go on and on.

Why does ice cream melt?

Why does summer have to end?

How come kittens have to grow up and be cats?

Flowers wilt, and best friends move away,
and when people get very old, they die.

I don't see why.

My grandpa says that we're like caterpillars.

They crawl around and think that being caterpillars is the best life there could ever be.

Then they start to change, and pretty soon they're all wrapped up in gray cocoons and look as though they're dead, for days and days.

Then guess what? They come out butterflies!
A hundred times more beautiful than
caterpillars, and they can *fly!*

If they'd gone on and on the way they were, they never would have had those wings.

My grandpa says that everything has to change and everything has to die, except one thing.

There's one thing that goes on and on forever, and it never changes and it never dies—God's love.

And God's love is a hundred times better than ice cream or summer or kittens or flowers or best friends.

When the time comes for people to die, God has another life all ready for them, a hundred times more wonderful than they could ever imagine, because God's love goes on forever.

God's Love Is for Sharing

To Joshua Travis Caswell—
the more he shares his love,
the more he has.

God loves me.
I feel his love like sunlight
shining down on me.

But I want to know,
how can I love God back?
You can't give God a hug, or anything.

153

I'd like to talk to God the way
I talk to Dad.
I've got a lot of questions Dad can't answer.

I'd like to walk with God—
or better yet,
we'd ride our bikes together in the park
and look at all the trees and things he's made.

I'd like to give God something nice—
my lop-eared rabbit, maybe.

Or a beautiful bouquet.
Of course, the flowers are his already,
and the rabbits, too.
How can you give God anything
when everything is his already?

You can't even share your ice cream with God.

But I could share with *someone*, couldn't I?

I know someone who would like a hug.

And I know someone who would like a kiss.

And if he's careful, there's someone
I'll even let play with my lop-eared rabbit.

And I will say to God,
"I loved you lots today,
the only way that I know how to do it."

God won't answer me exactly,
not like other people do
because that's not his way.
But I will know he's listening
because he loves me.